For Ben, Blaise and Garth

Illustrations are by Ben, Blaise and Garth Hall.

WRANG~GAITES

or

Wrong~Way~Round Way

A Play for Children of all ages

by

John Hall

THE LIZARD PRESS

J.S.B.N. A16712

X7/HAL
3
1029944

FIRST PUBLISHED JUNE 1st, 1973.

© 1973 by John Hall Plays Ltd.

Printed by Rainbow Enterprises, Bogenjoss House, Kirkhill, Dy

L820
508 683

9.73

'Wrang-Gaites' was first performed by York Theatre Royal Activists on May 5th 1973 at York, with the following cast :

George	Joe Sykes
Bruce	Stewart Illingworth
Roland	Dick Davey
Ellen	Jill Price
Queen	Kathy Gibson
Merlin	Carol Archer
Hen-Wife (Isla)	Moira Clampitt
Horse-Herd (Sir Tarnash)	Rob Adkins
Cow-Herd (Cowie)	Andy Bedell
Cripple	Nigel Fonseca
Elf King	Tim Southall
Old Woman	Ailsa Porteous
Gaoler	Ian Dickson
Princess from Greenland	Alison Sherriff
Princess from Cathay	Carole Jackson

Musicians, Guards, Populace, Monsters : Michael Cluff, Sarah Consitt, Rachel Day, Christine Farrow, Anne Fisher, Louise Gee, Jill Golledge, Linda Hordern, Marguerite Kamstra, Dinah Lawton, Sarah Pearsall, Jacqueline Penrose, Carole Philpin, Fiona Trobridge, Jane Turnbull, Debbie Whitehouse, Liz Woolley, Julie Wilson.

Sound	Colin Black
Properties	Graham East
	Kathy Gott
	Richard Smith
Production	Gerald Chapman

There is a slim-line version for a company of six players. See the back pages.

'Wrang-Gaites' is a children's play (for all ages, as the saying goes) which I can imagine giving a lot of pleasure both to the actors playing it and to the audience watching and listening. It is in the nature of a slapstick 'Sword in the Stone', hitting out a spark of poetry every now and then as it gallops along, and with great chances for a director's ingenuity. It is as though the traditional Mummer's Play of St. George and the Dragon had spread and ramified and leaped into the twentieth century.'

Christopher Fry.

———

What the critics have said about some of John Hall's other plays:

'Mr. Hall is clearly a man who cannot be disregarded' - Harold Hobson, The Sunday Times.

'He thunders out ideas while other writers can only mew. He can rasp at the mind and besiege the heart' - Desmond Pratt, Yorkshire Post.

'The debut of a new dramatic talent which - I have no hesitation in risking the prophecy - will go far.' T.C. Worsley, New Statesman.

'John Hall's 'THE STRANGERS' . . . the sort of new play that theatregoers ought to flock to.' Norman Shrapnel, The Guardian.

'He is a realistic visionary' - J.C. Trewin, Birmingham Post.

THE CHARACTERS

GEORGE

BRUCE

ROLAND

ELLEN

QUEEN

MERLIN

COWIE

SIR TARNASH

ISLA

CRIPPLE

OLD WOMAN

ELF KING

PORTER OF THE DARK TOWER

PRINCESS OF CATHAY

ICE MAIDEN

PEOPLE, SERVANTS, DRUMMER,
PALACE GUARD, MONSTERS

ACT ONE

The Court of Grampia - the garden.

The Holy Scanda Stone is U.C. - very old and raglish. There is also a rustic seat with royal quarterings.
Three sons of the Royal House of Scandanna are playing a disorderly game of Foot-the-Ball.

GEORGE. Pass, Roland! Get your feet to it, Bruce! Now then, lads, I'm going to intercept you!

BRUCE. Skeut, Roland! Ach, ye skair-leukin' skribbie! Skeut, skeut!

ROLAND. I am skeuting!

GEORGE. *(Gets ball)* It's a matter of positioning. *(Dribbles ball round the stone clockwise; shouts joyously)* A sudden break by George! How confidently he deals with Roland's shot!

BRUCE. *(Charges to meet him the other way - roars)* I'll intercept ye, Georgie, ye skeut-fittit Pirrlie-weeack!

ROLAND. Wrang-gaites, Bruce! You're going wrang-gaites! Take care, Big Brother! *(Pulls him back. They topple, and roll like puppies. George foots the ball decorously round the stone.)*

GEORGE. The Dons scored with their beautiful left wing manoeuvre. They always looked the more dangerous side. This is decorative, pattern-weaving play, lads. Pretty, outfield pattern-weaving. Tight and confident. This is it, lads! This is what makes Foot-the-Ball the King of Spectator Sports. *(BURD ELLEN enters. She is excessively pretty. She is all pink and gold. She walks with an ineffable English superiority. Her alert features adapt to braw-mannered youths of the Scottish Court she is on a visit to, as a part of very imprecise marriage arrangements. She has very long, golden, elaborately dressed hair. She is totally unselfconscious and wickedly demure.)*

GEORGE. *(continued)* Oh hullo, Burd Ellen. Watch this! A sudden break by pattern-weaving George has the rival goal in

danger. He worms his way past Hermiston at the six-yard line!
(Eludes imaginary player)

ELLEN.   George! *(GEORGE stops. BRUCE and ROLAND sit
up)* I like greyhound coursing. I have my great dog Girdelin at
my father's court, George. It has such a long slender body, its
eyes are so keen, it can go like the wind.

BRUCE.   Nay, ye have griffins. I'm thinking ye keepit a pirl
wee griffin in Somerset, Burd Ellen!

ELLEN.   And falconry is our great sport too! We take goshawks
young from the nest. They are tamed with jesses. A good hawk
will fly off your fist and soar to a great height and check there.
She waits for her quarry, high, high above your head.

ROLAND.   She?

GEORGE.   *(informative)* With all birds of prey the females are
invariably larger and more powerful than the males.

ELLEN.   Of course! Sometimes she will get her prey by rising
above it in the air, and stooping to strike it to the ground!
(pause) Sometimes we go hawking for larks.

ROLAND.   That's a song-bird!

ELLEN.   We eat them.

GEORGE.   I defer to none in my admiration for the English
Court which has sent us Burd Ellen. Our ways must seem rough
to the civilised South. But really - eating larks!

BRUCE.   Ye nivver heard such a rabblach! She's a giddy quainey
She-giants in Somerset next-aye, dressed in sarkits an' ridin'
with hawkies as high as a mannie's leg!

ELLEN.   *(laughing)* Bruce, don't say these things!

GEORGE.   You overdo the Banffshire dialect, old man. Nobody
doubts your patriotic zeal -

BRUCE.   *(shouts)* I'm no safty on the bit lassie from the English
Court, if that's what you mean, George.

ELLEN.   We never know what you mean, Kinsman Bruce.

BRUCE.   I'm no kinsman of yours, Burd Ellen!

ELLEN.   Pardon me, I thought we were one big happy royal
family - even if we do cut off a few heads.

ROLAND. *(who likes political discussions)* There has to be some pruning in the gardens of Albion!

GEORGE. Have to dead-head a few roses - ha! ha!

ELLEN. Despite which, Bruce dear, I like your style - you're a fine patriot, and so am I!

GEORGE. *(sententiously)* Patriotism is the last refuge of the scoundrel.

ELLEN. That hasn't been said yet. *(To BRUCE)* I'm sure there would soon be a race of terrible giants around, Bruce, if you came to Somerset. *(collapsing with laughter)* Only, I don't know what you say!

BRUCE. I say nothing to you, Burd Ellen, and I'll direct you to my bonnie brother George - for it's him you were posted up north to!

ROLAND. Careful, Bruce - you're nearly talking English!

(Enter QUEEN and MERLIN)

BRUCE. I nae speakit unknown tongues, an' leerracht aff as muckle lig-laggin' as some!

(They start a cheery wrestling bout on the strength of it.)

QUEEN. Children!

(GEORGE rises from stone. His brothers desist.)

GEORGE. Mother, please - I'm eighteen!

QUEEN. Oh George, I didn't see you.

BRUCE. I'm seventeen. That's old enough for a suit of armour!

QUEEN. Oh Bruce, you shall have one!

ROLAND. I'm sixteen. What can I have, Mother?

BRUCE. A hobby horse!

GEORGE. Muzzle a moment, Bruce - no-one's asking you.

QUEEN. Perhaps you can have Burd Ellen!

GEORGE. Oh now, hang on a moment, Mother, that's not too funny, you know. Everybody knows Ellen is my bride.

ELLEN. I don't.

GEORGE. *(airily)* I had rather not go into details, Burd Ellen, but, joking apart, I undoubtedly have my position to consider. You were definitely invited to the Court of Grampia to marry me.

I don't want to make a thing of it.

ELLEN. But you're such a good footballer, I can't think what you want with me!

GEORGE. *(sniffily)* There are limits, you know. *(Retires behind Scanda Stone.)*

QUEEN. Merlin Caledonius! How are we to shuffle them?

MERLIN. Majesty has some good cards. The King of Greenland has a daughter. She is shudderingly sweet. Ambassadors arrived last week and are thawing out nicely. The Ice Maiden is to follow, subject to satisfactory unfreezing arrangements.

QUEEN. What do you think?

MERLIN. *(taking his time)* Then, Majesty, may I remind you that the Mongolian Delegation has arrived with a very lengthy caravan full of the treasures of the East. It has taken them a whole year to get here.

QUEEN. But they are so tired you haven't liked to ask them the purpose of their visit.

MERLIN. Yes, I've found out now.

BRUCE. Have they brought engines of war, fireworks and the like? Perhaps they're for me?

GEORGE. Have they brought Manuals of Good Government and Garments for State Occasions - they'll be for me!

MERLIN. Far at the rear of this caravanserai is a great - what d'you call it -

QUEEN. He's old - he forgets words.

MERLIN. You know, one of those royal litter things - one of those what's-its -

ROLAND. A Howdah!

BRUCE. Aye - an unco-leukin' carriage to cuddle quaineys in!

MERLIN. Quiet, yocho! Yes, it was a howdah - with a canopy of cloth of gold. It can only contain an oriental princess.

GEORGE. Well, Mother, your money troubles and dynastic worries seem to be over. We have an Ice-maiden from Greenland and a Princess from Cathay at the end of a caravan of presents half a mile long -

QUEEN. Oh George, if it was as simple as that!

GEORGE. As simple as what, Mother?

BRUCE. Just line these princesses up, Mother, and - puddle-doo! The frog can jump in the cream!

MERLIN. Yallta! These are serious matters. The lovely princess of Avalon will forgive the crude expressions of Banffshire bullyboys.

QUEEN. Bruce - your house will hold a hoyden. Take him away, George. He bubbles like a coconut.

GEORGE. But I'll be back, Mother! I won't deprive you of my princely mind.

BRUCE. You won't rodger me. Ye will get an awfou mischief, George! *(GEORGE hustles him off)*

GEORGE. Ooff!

QUEEN. My boys are brawny. But Ellen, there's one with a brain to him. Do you like her, Roland?

ROLAND. I do not like to say.

ELLEN. I do not need a mirror to tell me I am fair. I keep my state in secret, laughing to my sweet self.

MERLIN. Your coffers are empty, Majesty. Since the good old king went away -

ROLAND. Where did he go, Mother, my Father, the good old king?

QUEEN. Merlin knows, Merlin knows.

MERLIN. Ah, Majesty! *(heavily)* I am now a very old magician, and I forget nearly everything.

ELLEN. How old, Merlin Caledonius?

MERLIN. I am about 900 years old. I am very weary. I can only remember a very few spells now. Everything is such an effort.

ROLAND. Wrang-gaites he went, didn't he? Wrang-gaites my Royal Dad went round the stone, the opposite way to the sun, and was never heard of again!

MERLIN. I suppose so. I really don't know. I could find out, if I made a fearful effort. But Majesty has not pressed me.

QUEEN. One manages. Some things are best left alone.

ELLEN. But you haven't managed - that's the point. You've got

no money! That's why you keep at it on the Royal and Ancient
Marriage Mart.

MERLIN.   The young princess from Avalon is not slow on the
uptake.

ROLAND.   Chivalry bids me seek out my Dad, Ellen. It makes
me shudder, though. *(Takes her to one side)* He is in Elfland.
He is in the Dark Tower of the King of Elfland!

ELLEN.   How absolutely frightful. You must get him out!

ROLAND.   Yes, but I am a peaceable boy. I like to sit and read
on the Stone. I like to think out serious questions. I puzzle over
how I will counter my brothers' invincible ignorance, and set
things to rights in my darling Mother's muddle of a land.

ELLEN..   I expect we shall have to have some proper
conversations. Isn't that old magician any good? I like his
beard. He must know something.

ROLAND.   Yes, but he can't remember it.

ELLEN.   Merlin! What shall I tell the Somerset witches that
Scottish magicians are worth?

MERLIN.   You speak jestingly, Princess of Avalon. *(Proudly)*
I am the first of the warlocks. I can tell the shape of time.
If Roland and Burd Ellen will venture into the dismal halls of
time, they shall not lack Merlin's aid.

QUEEN.   Decent old man! And now I think we will leave you two
young things to play together. Come, Merlin.

MERLIN.   Majesty! *(They go off)*
*(ROLAND clambers onto the Scanda Stone. He sits cross-
legged looking U.C.)*

ROLAND.   Do you see?

ELLEN.   What?

ROLAND.   Do you not see? Over there, where the sun dies.
Beyond that tall, scalped mountain, where the two hills crouch,
like two bulls locked horn in horn. Oh, I've spent a lifetime
gazing upon that sight!

ELLEN.   Ye-es. It's somewhat as you say.

ROLAND.   A Castle squats there, sick as a toad, blind as a

fool's heart, blackened, rack'd with storm - for the storms all come from over there.

ELLEN. *(Chin upon hand, leans beside him on the Stone)* Adventurers would be lost, for ever, going that way.

ROLAND. They are. Many of them are. My father one, a goodly knight, my father Giles Scandanna, the King of Grampia. Spit upon and cursed.

ELLEN. Why?

ROLAND. All were under spells, honest frank knightly souls -

ELLEN. *(Coolly)* Oh, you have them in Scotland?

ROLAND. You are a mothiewart. Except you have pretty hair.

ELLEN. I am a king's daughter!

ROLAND. Burd Ellen, when I blow my golden horn at the side of the mountain, I shall see them then - I shall see and know them all! And yet I may never see Middle Earth again if I go there.

ELLEN. Oh but you will! I'll tell you why too! Because you are the youngest son, who is not too conceited, or thinks himself smarter than other folks, but is kind and polite and humble and generous, and very very courteous to ladies.

ROLAND. *(Laughs)* Seriously?

ELLEN. *(They are settling down to this)* Oh, I can assure you you must take it very very seriously, or I for one can have nothing to do with you whatever.

ROLAND. Yes, but listen - this courtesie you're talking about - this very parfit gentle knight stuff - well, nowadays that's only taken up by flabby persons, a rather knock-kneed variety. It's all right, I dare say, for the beautiful and virtuous ladies to whom they have to vow service -

ELLEN. Roland, you've got it all wrong! Look, we can agree about this, can't we? - chivalry is maintained to succour distressed damsels and to destroy tyrants. Knights have to seek foemen worthy of their steel and they've got to do mighty deeds like rescuing these maidens from dragons and all that, but it's strength of character that counts.

ROLAND. *(Disgustedly)* You sound exactly like George. What

a pair you'll make.

ELLEN. *(Stamps foot)* I don't sound like George. You don't know what I am like - not one little bit. *(Pause)* I had a very good and holy man at home to teach me the secrets of the heart. I see a magical future for myself and I shall make several men quite unhappy.

ROLAND. Hurrah! My brother George is not the man for you! Why do you want to collar a man anyway? What do you want with a high prince?

ELLEN. I want to go on adventures! You need a prince for that - if you're a princess.

ROLAND. Shall we adopt disguises. How would that be? You can be my squire. A prince is supposed to have one.

ELLEN. Oh - let us start quickly!

(Pause)

ROLAND. That is just talk, of course. I only really want to sit here, and dream.

(Reads. ELLEN kicks the ball idly. It rolls U.C. beyond the stone and out of sight. She runs round the stone in search of it. ROLAND looks up and sees what she is doing)

Burd Ellen - you must not do that. You are running wranggaites round the stone. That is what my royal Dad did. He went around the Holy Stone the opposite way to the sun.

ELLEN. Oh you superstitious Scots!

ROLAND. *(Sharply)* Have your Somerset witches taught you nothing? You will be carried off by the fairies. It will take the boldest Knight in Christendom to bring you back.

ELLEN. What tremendous fun! You'll come and fetch me, won't you, Roland - it's just what you're cut out for - it's your destiny, my dear boy!

ROLAND. You don't ask much, do you?

ELLEN. Of course! I ask far too much! That's the whole point, isn't it? *(Puffs to a halt beside him)* Well, you needn't worry, I only ran round just the once.

ROLAND. That's quite enough, according to some authorities.

ELLEN. Well, I'm still here, aren't I? But the ball has
rolled out of sight somewhere - perhaps in those bushes!

ROLAND. You mothie-wart - that's our best ball - burrow in
and find it!

ELLEN. You are not gentle. This is not chivalrous talk,
young Roland.

ROLAND. It's gentle but not genteel. *(Kisses her. She shrieks
and runs. He chases her)* Not so fast!
(ELLEN stops dead. He stops dead. He stares at her.)

ELLEN. Roland!

ROLAND. What's the matter?

ELLEN. I'm frightened. Something is happening to me. What
is that terrible noise? It catches me up and flings me across
the plain - I am dragged after it! It's like all the noises I have
ever heard in my life - and coming all together!

ROLAND. *(Holding her)* It is only some trick!

ELLEN. *(Faintly)* The trap shuts. *(Shrieks)* Solve it, you!
I am inside the den!

ROLAND. Burd Ellen! Burd Ellen!
(Lights dim.
Elves and sprites spirit her away.   Faery music.
Lights come up again slowly.
*MERLIN, BRUCE, GEORGE, the QUEEN, look at the body of
the young prince splayed across the holy stone)*

GEORGE. He'll come round in a minute, I expect, Mother. I
expect he fell and hit his head. But where's Ellen? That's
odd.

QUEEN. Be quiet, George. What do you think, Merlin
Caledonius? *(Caressing ROLAND's face)* My wee balloch loon!

BRUCE. Logies! Are ye dead, Roland?

GEORGE. He's coming round, I think.

BRUCE. Gee'n a guid fauchan, Mother. Rub him up a bitty.
He's bin awa' i' the fairy hillock.

MERLIN. There is something in what Prince Bruce says,
Majesty. He has the look of it.

ROLAND. *(Coming round)* Ellen! Burd Ellen!

QUEEN. What is it, my sweet? What have you done with Burd Ellen? What have you to tell us?

ROLAND. She's gone, she's gone! *(Subsides weakly in QUEEN's arms)* Oh Mother - a grinding, a gripping - she was pinched and clutched! A great hook came down out of the skies! Aie! Aie!

GEORGE. The moment my back is turned! Roland, you might have hallooed out or something. At all events, it is my plain duty to go and retrieve my bride.

BRUCE. I'll raise a body of men. We'll back-jaw the grizzly gryphons!

GEORGE. *(Annoyed)* Bruce, you seem to think you're the only one who can stand up and fight anybody. I am perfectly capable of rescuing Burd Ellen. *(Fussily)* I suppose she went wrang-gaites round the Stone. We really want to get rid of that Stone, you know, Mother. It's simply a disgrace, having a thing like that so near the house. It's a frightful hazard to visiting princesses. I can't go rescuing them all, you know. We should definitely move it further from the house.

QUEEN. If only we could! But Merlin says no.

MERLIN. The House of Scandanna will fall if you do, Majesty. I am afraid that is just one of the facts of life.

GEORGE. I shall require a good briefing from you, Merlin Caledonius, on the geography of Elfland and the various tests I may expect to undergo. And if it is possible to bring her back, I'll do it, or perish in the attempt.

MERLIN. Possible it is. But woe to the man or mother's son that attempts it, if he is not well taught beforehand what he is to do.

GEORGE. Precisely, Merlin Caledonius - so I'll be glad if you'll get on with it.

(The PEOPLE enter and eye GEORGE anxiously. - They will come in to eye the proceedings anxiously from time to time because all these things are more important to them than you

might think)

QUEEN. Oh George - dear dignified, absurd, kingly, George -
am I really to let you go? I really don't know about this,
Merlin Caledonius - it's asking an awful lot of a queen who
lost the best of husbands the same way.

GEORGE. *(Stoutly)* I am not to be put off, Mother.

QUEEN. Take then, my son, your father's good brand that
never struck in vain.

(Servants approach bearing the good brand on its ornamental
stand. GEORGE puts hand out to it. He yanks it. It does
not budge. An awkward silence)

GEORGE. No thank you, Mother. I have an awfully good two-
handed sword - run and fetch it, Bruce!

(BRUCE hurries off)

Presented to me, as the High Prince, if you remember, Mother,
by the King of Ferrara. It is very good for single combat.

QUEEN. Yes Darling, but how do you know elves 'stick to
single combat? I really think your father's good brand that
never struck in vain might be better. If only he'd had it with
him at the time of his unfortunate lapse it might have been a
very different story.

(BRUCE staggers in with two-handed sword. GEORGE takes
it. It is rather heavy so he gives it back to BRUCE to hold
for the present. The QUEEN admires the sword)

It's very nice. Pity it hasn't got any magical powers. Merlin,
say a spell over it that will give it victory, will you?

MERLIN. I'll do what I can, Majesty. Lay the Sword on the
Stone, Prince Bruce. I will come to it by and by. First I
have a few simple instructions for your brother the High Prince.

GEORGE. Thank you, thank you. I am really rather pressed
for time, Merlin. There is a good deal of protocol to be gone
through. Just instruct me briefly as you can, old man.

MERLIN. Well my son, there are but two things. Simple they
may seem, but hard they are to do. One thing to do and one
thing not to do. And the thing to do is this: after you have

entered the land of Faery, whoever speaks to you, you must cut off their head. And what you've not to do is this : bite no bit, and drink no drop, however hungry or thirsty you be; drink a drop or bite a bit, while in Elfland you be, and never will you see Middle Earth again . . . . One more thing. If you should ever want me, it is possible - at least it used to be possible . .

(Scratches head, goes to examine Sword on Stone, to hide his embarrassment. He remains apart, making caballistic signs over the two-handed Sword during the following.

GEORGE prepares to leave.

This is a complicated process. Due form has to be observed. A trumpet flourish off-stage.

A drummer enters to GEORGE.

The people nod and point to the drummer approvingly. The drummer positions himself drumming away busily.)

GEORGE. That's enough, Drummer! Plenty of time for that, you know. Now for my armour. Bruce, you have to pass me things in the right order.

(Servants bring armour. They pass them to BRUCE and BRUCE passes them to GEORGE. The servants assist in the accoutrement itself.)

Greaves!

BRUCE. Greaves!

SERVANT. Greaves!

BRUCE. Thigh-piece!

SERVANT. Thigh-piece!

BRUCE. Arm-piece!

SERVANT. Arm-piece!

BRUCE. Elbow-piece!

SERVANT. Elbow-piece!

BRUCE. Knee-piece!

SERVANT. Knee-piece!

BRUCE. Breast-plate!

SERVANT. Breast-plate!

BRUCE. Gorget!

SERVANT. Gorget!

BRUCE. Helmet!

SERVANT. Helmet!

BRUCE. Belt!

SERVANT. Belt!

(GEORGE tries his armour for movement)

GEORGE. I wonder if I need a lance-rest? This is a bit tight under the arm. *(Servant makes adjustment)* Well, I don't suppose I'll need a lance, not with my great two-handed Ferrara. Is my horse armoured?

BRUCE. Doun the brae, George. Doun the brae. Will ye hodge as far as that?

(GEORGE takes a few paces in a stately manner)

GEORGE. My sword!

(MERLIN gives up Sword to BRUCE who carries it to GEORGE)

MERLIN. It is heavily bound with my best spells. I still have some skill. It should now be immune from most systems of attack.

GEORGE. *(Not in a hurry to take it)* That is satisfactory. Have you any further advice for me, Warlock Merlin?

MERLIN. Yes! It is important to leave none of your equipment in fairyland. The elves will try to steal things - tassets, tuilles, sollerets - anything they can get hold of. You will never get back to Middle Earth if you leave any part of your royal equipment in that dusty thoroughfare.

GEORGE. Oh - my drummer will have to pick anything up. Bruce!

(BRUCE kneels)

BRUCE. Fare furth the gate, brother! I'm pipean for ye! *(greets)*

GEORGE. Bruce! As Prince Imperial and Heir Preparent, you will now take precedence, saving only Majesty herself, our beloved Mother. If you marry in my absence your wife will take the same rank as yourself.

BRUCE. I'm no' thinking of that, George! *(Greets noisily)*

GEORGE. There are two princesses expected at court, who

will be looking you over, the one from Greenland, and the other from Cathay. Mother, you will see that the general order and good conduct of the Court is maintained in the absence of the High Prince, no doubt.

QUEEN. Please don't worry, darling! You will have enough on your mind without that.

(GEORGE kisses his mother - the armour just permits the embrace. The QUEEN subsides into her rustic seat, slightly overcome by it all)

GEORGE. *(grandly)* Fare forth!

(Pats ROLAND on his way out. The blow almost fells him)

Fare forth!

(GEORGE takes sword from BRUCE)

Fare forth!

(Bears it aloft)

Fare forth!

(Exit GEORGE. The drummer follows, drumming like mad. Trumpet flourishes. The people cheer. The QUEEN rises)

QUEEN. Good people! The Prince George has gone, as a good prince must, to rescue the fair Burd Ellen from the Dark Tower of the King of Elfland. Everything is as it should be. He will go by the pine tree and beside the wild rose bush, and he will come to the desolate way at last, for which he set out. And that will lead to Elfland. And you must all pray that your noble prince will overcome many dangers and will gather all his strength together when he reaches the Dark Tower, where with mighty blows he will strike against the rock, again and again!

(The people nod appreciatively and go out. The Guard squat down and the servants, and they are thinking hard about all this and perhaps they are praying, with BRUCE and ROLAND in the midst.

But the QUEEN waits in her rustic seat, a very composed figure. She may have some sewing. MERLIN leans against the Stone with his book of spells. He riffles the pages, and he reflects. He groans now and then.

BRUCE breaks the spell of silence)

BRUCE.   A doot the thing'll mis-gae.

ROLAND.   And it's your turn next!

(Pause)

BRUCE.   Puir George.   He's a muckle little man.   He shouldna ha gang.

ROLAND.   *(Cheerfully)* We depend on you now, Bruce.

(Pause. MERLIN turns to the QUEEN.   He bends his old knee to her.   He's very shaky.)

MERLIN.   Majesty, alas!

QUEEN.   No remedy, no spell, no conjuration?   Can you find nothing, recall nothing from your very long and misty past, old counsellor?

MERLIN.   My secrets have returned to their source.   Be done with me, Majesty!

QUEEN.   No, I don't think I shall quite be done with you . . . All the same . . . .

Long we have waited and longer still,

With doubt and muckle pain -

And woe are the hearts of his brethren

For he comes not back again!

(BRUCE leaps up.

The People enter and eye him anxiously.)

BRUCE.   *(Almost forgetting his Banffshire dialect in his eagerness)* Let me go, Mother!   I shall organise a body of men.   The Palace Guard will do.

(The Palace Guard cheers wildly)

We will crack all the skulls between here and the Dark Tower -
an' we'll rescue a' the lost adventurers - and Faythur - an'
Burd Ellen - an' High Prince George an' a'!

(The People grow wildly excited.

BRUCE drills the Guard.

A Piper enters, piping like anything.

The QUEEN rises - Court Servants approach bearing the good brand)

QUEEN. Bruce dear - you had better take your father's good brand. If George had taken the brand, it might have been a different story.

(BRUCE puts out his hand to grasp the brand. He yanks at it. It does not budge. An awkward silence)

BRUCE. Nae mair aboot it. Thee're maikin' a t'dee nae common aboot that thing, Mother.

ROLAND. Durindal, brother! - the blade that never struck in vain! No notch upon the edge, nor scratch or dent upon the blade! If I were going -

BRUCE. *(Furiously)* Well, you're nae gang! Ye deavin' cretur, Roland. Mother, save your Majesty, it would be an indulgence to take the brand. Fur a'm high eneuch to hoch-hicht that dyke!

QUEEN. He's a confident lad, Merlin. All may yet be well.

(Martial music.
BRUCE and his pipers and his guardsmen march off.
The QUEEN returns to her sewing.
MERLIN mutters over his spell-book.
ROLAND climbs up onto the Stone to watch BRUCE's progress across the plain. He waves to BRUCE. Martial music fades into bird-song.
Stillness.
The QUEEN rises.
The QUEEN goes to the Scanda Stone.
The QUEEN speaks:)

QUEEN. What is the sound that I hear in the forest?

(MERLIN riffles pages of spell-book)

MERLIN. *(mutters)* Dreadful nags - toads and wild-cats - groaning oaks - I can't make any sense of it.

ROLAND. He has come to a high stone wall. The thorn trees stoop down. They pass beyond the wall. I see no more.

QUEEN. The trees are murmuring quietly together. Among the grass and the flowers are soft sweet little voices - my boy cannot always hear them, but he is so happy because he knows they are there. All at once he hears music that he has never heard before.

(Music we have never heard before.

MERLIN cries out.

He strikes his spell-book against the stone)

QUEEN. He's getting through!

MERLIN. Ooh aah. Chum choo. Ooh aah. Chum choo.

QUEEN. We must be patient with him.

(Pause)

MERLIN. *(Upright again and dignified)* Never have I been so
  troubled, Majesty, since the Scallawags pursued me across the
  Tweed, and I was impaled for a night and a day on a hidden
  stake in the burn at Drummalzier! The hostile rustics thought
  I was Mungo Kentigern. I have felt again the throbbing pains
  of the onslaught - but not of Scallawags - of elves, eldritches,
  bats and spiders! Majesty, alas! The Grampian Guard has
  been defeated by spiders! With my own eyes I have seen it,
  on my own body they set their slimy souvenirs.

QUEEN. How horrible!

MERLIN. Yes, it was, Majesty. *(Raises hands)* Woe to his
  mother's and brother's heart, for he comes not back again!

ROLAND. Now, Mother dear, you see the case we're in.

QUEEN. Long have we waited and longer still, with muckle
  doubt and pain!

ROLAND. But you've still got me, haven't you - the last and
  dearest of your children.

QUEEN. If you are lost, all is lost!

ROLAND. But I am alive and well and living in Banffshire.

QUEEN. I was afraid for a moment you were going after Burd
  Ellen and your brothers and your long lost father too - taking
  with you your father's good brand that never struck in vain.

ROLAND. Yes. *(Thoughtfully)* I suppose I am really.

(The People enter and eye him anxiously.

ROLAND grins back at them)

Oh well. I'll go, if you all insist.

PEOPLE. We all insist!

ROLAND. After all, I am definitely quite fond of Burd Ellen.

PEOPLE. Definitely!

ROLAND. And we were having such an interesting conversation.

PEOPLE. You were, you were!

QUEEN. Go then, my son. I would deny you if I could. I have grown tired of disasters. Two sons gone!

(The People greet)

And the best of husbands - the good king -

(The People greet a bit more)

The best of husbands, as I say, and King of all Grampia, but foolish in some ways - and inclined to show off in front of visitors. Accompanied a passing Dervish Dancer round the Holy Stone. She twirled so fast she outspun the spell. But the best of husbands was caught by his royal coat-tails. Your brothers will be greeting with him now, in some glum gap of time - some daylight-less dungeon. But I see you are set on going.

(Court Servants offer the brand.)

Raise it, dearest of boys!

(ROLAND raises Durindal without difficulty)

ROLAND. *(Testing it)* Yes - I think this will suit me nicely, Mother.

(She girds it on him)

QUEEN. Go, child Roland! Go quickly as thou mayest. Yet first cross your beautiful white hands upon your breast, that a mother may bless you.

ROLAND. *(Kneels)* Willingly, Mother. Say the spell that will give me victory, won't you?

(She says the spell.

The People rejoice)

PEOPLE. Roland! Roland! Win man, and win maid, and guard our faith, as thou was ever ready.

MERLIN. *(Shakes his head wearily)* Give Roland his golden horn!

(Servant gives horn)

When you come to the Dark Tower, Child Roland, blow thrice,
and strike the rock with your good brand. It will not break.

ROLAND. *(Heroically)* Then Holy Mary, Mother of Heaven,
come to my aid! And Father God pardon me for all the wrong
that I have done in great things and in small. Through Jesu
Grace shall I be pardoned for all I have done from the hour of
my birth!

(He goes.

QUEEN alone with MERLIN.

She sews.

*MERLIN sinks down heavily against the Stone - His Book of
Spells falls from his hand.)*

QUEEN. Merlin - the Princesses.

MERLIN. *(Sighs)* It's a problem.

QUEEN. They have come for husbands.

MERLIN. From Greenland and Cathay!

QUEEN. Beguile them. Tell them a story. Say I have sent
my sons on heroic journeys to test their suitability for
princesses - from Greenland and Cathay.

MERLIN. Yes, Majesty. *(Glumly)* Such expensive guests -
disastrous!

QUEEN. One does not know where to turn these days.

MERLIN. What with Scallawags and Dundees at each others'
throats - and at mine - and this extreme old age of mine, and -
oh bother!

(The QUEEN smiles)

QUEEN. He looked so distinctive!

END OF ACT ONE

ACT TWO

Scene One - The Heath.

COW-HERD, HORSE-HERD, HEN-WIFE.

COW-HERD has cowlike aspects, HORSE has horselike, HEN henny. They are still, however, recognisably human: as though deformed in these ways.

They are on a barren heath. The COW-HERD lies with his head in the couch-grass, snoring. The HEN-WIFE clucks on the path. The HORSE-HERD is grazing his horses within sight. The HEN-WIFE stops and sniffs at the COW-HERD. She is a ragged female of uncertain age. The COW-HERD is a stout young rustic. His fodder-bag is beside him. He has eaten and swilled and now he is snoring it off.

HEN-WIFE. *(calls)* Horse-Herd!

HORSE-HERD. Hen-Wife? What have you found on the dusty thoroughfare? *(kindly)* You look as if you had waddled far. Shall you roost in a tree? Night is coming.

HEN-WIFE. Fat lot of trees here for roosting in! *(Sniffs COW-HERD)* They'll have him at this rate. They know some tricks to play on the likes of him!

HORSE-HERD. *(Sighs)* It is a bad time in a bad country, Mistress Hen-Wife. And no champion forthcoming.

HEN-WIFE. *(Insinuates)* Oh sir, with your free and graceful air, you need not fear the eldritches! *(Kicks COW-HERD who snorts loudly but doesn't wake)* They'll carry this one off, if he stays snorting much longer. Serve him right, the guzzler! I've had nothing all day. *(Helps herself from COW-HERD's fodder-bag)*

HORSE-HERD. *(Sighs again)* He comes not, he comes not. *(Moves away, gazes into the distance)*

HEN-WIFE.   What champion could we expect, you noble-minded
 horse-herd?   *(Bitterly)* We cannot help our case.

(HORSE-HERD stamps and whinnies)

HORSE-HERD.   One comes! One comes!   A finer looking fellow
 I have never seen!

(ROLAND enters)

HEN-WIFE.   *(Clucks round)*   O Lord, O Lord, that I should have
 seen this sorrowful day!

ROLAND.   Why, what's the matter?

HEN-WIFE.   I am a hen-wife who has lost all her chicks.

ROLAND.   Tell me the way, Hen-Wife, to the Dark Tower of the
 King of Elfland!

HEN-WIFE.   Aie!   What if I do?   You will only chop me up for
 dinner!   Aie!   I know you young knights what comes asking
 such questions.   I do not want to die in this bare and barren
 heath.   Spare a poor old Hen-Wife who has lost all her chikkeys.

HORSE-HERD.   *(Canters up)*   She has no remnant of truth in
 her.   She ate her own eggs.   Yet would you credit it, sir, she
 once had a warm heart and enjoyed a kindly sense of attachment
 to her fowl kind.

ROLAND.   What or who or why are you?   I see you have hooves.

HORSE-HERD.   Ruin is all my tale.   All in the dusty thoroughfare moulder and decay, lamenting far off days.   I will direct
 you to the King's Tower.   You must shut your eyes while I do
 so.   Then you can open them quickly and smite off my head.

ROLAND.   Very well.   *(Closes his eyes)*

HORSE-HERD.   Within less than a hundred leagues, upon the
 right or the left or straight ahead or behind you, you will see a
 hoary cripple.   He has a rough staff in his hand.   He can point
 you the way into that ominous tract which, all agree, leads to
 the Dark Tower.

*(He kneels before ROLAND, baring his neck.   He speaks
 rapidly)*

The Hen-Wife will instruct you next.   But you will have to
bribe her, for she has lost command of her character.   Strike

now, I beg you. I cannot assist you any more.

(ROLAND opens his eyes. He looks with astonishment at the kneeling HORSE-HERD)

ROLAND. Strike Durindal!

(He strikes at the HORSE-HERD, who falls lifeless. He turns to the HEN-WIFE, who runs round him, clucking.)

Now, Hen-Wife! What have you got to tell me. I am Roland of Scandanna. I can pay you well.

(HEN-WIFE clucks and circles madly)

HEN-WIFE- The Round Square in the Black and White Lair is the place of strength! You must vault overhead and burrow and burrow! Scratch like me or fly like a fish you must! Then you come to the broad bartizan. It admits two persons, walking abreast. There is a line of seven windows and a six-sided form of fair proportions. But the second, fourth and sixth are three-sided. All was built up long ago. That is the only way, Prince Chick, to the Great Hall of the Castle where Burd Ellen lies enthralled . . . . Aie! But I do not want to die on this bare and barren heath. I have lost all my chickabiddies!

(Tugs at fodder-bag with her beak. Corn spills. Sits to gobble corn)

ROLAND. Strike, Durindal!

(He despatches her. She lies in a heap. ROLAND turns to the COW-HERD)

COW-HERD. *(In his sleep)* Gie us a dram! Ach - ye'll nivver! Stack in m'craig. Hauch it up! *(makes a sickening noise in throat)*

ROLAND. This must be the Cow-Herd. I will seize him by his horns.

(Pulls COW-HERD to his feet. The stout lad gazes wide-eyed)

COW-HERD. Claucht, am I? Dreeful day! Dinna loonder me!

ROLAND. I am Prince Roland of Scandanna, loon! Say what you know in plain terms. Hear me! I seek the way to find the fair Burd Ellen. Answer! You know your fate if you do not.

COW-HERD. *(Titters)* I know my fate if I do . . . . Whiel, whiel!

Ga by land and water. Harrow and rake. Pass the devil's cauldron and the cleft oak. The Great Back Bird will be the Guide you seek. You must stab and end the creature! In a sheet of flame at last, two hills on the right, you will see them all!

ROLAND. What hills, what hills?

COW-HERD. The hills of hell, master! Tis there you must go! *(Titters and collapses in obscene lump)* Venison pasty, fat buck and holy peas, and a plump cook maid!
(ROLAND fells the fat boy)

ROLAND. Now shrewd wit recall these things. I will press forward to my desire. *(Looks round)* What a gloomy place this is! I'll get along now.
(The HORSE-HERD, HEN-WIFE and COW-HERD all rise spectrally)

Heavens - have I to kill you again?

HORSE-HERD. Relieve us of our deformities! Misty vapours have passed from our eyes, Roland, and we see ourselves for what we are. *(Shivers horribly)*

HEN-WIFE. Let us follow and serve you on Wrang - Gaites Way, young Prince. We will serve for ever such a one as you.

COW-HERD. Away mid the mountains
      Where the heathcock wakes
      Leaping before thee, Roland, on the crag
      Young and middling and old
      You have saved us from sorcery
      We will serve you evermore.

ROLAND. Fine, but I can't wait a moment longer. *(They kneel)* Still - I was tired of my own company. You may come with me. *(Overjoyed at their deliverance the three leap up, hugging each other and dancing round. Then they kneel again quickly before he changes his mind)*

HORSE-HERD. I am Sir Tarnash.

HEN-WIFE. I am Isla.

COW-HERD. I am Cowie.

(ROLAND dismantles the hen's beak)

ISLA. Ooh, what a relief. I can speak my mind again.

(ROLAND dismantles the cow horns)

COWIE. Fussle up the ill-getit thang! *(tramples horns into ground)* I'm m'ain body and ah'll dee m'ain wark masel', master, thanks be the da' ye cam' to fytan me. *(Hugs ROLAND)*

ROLAND. *(Goodhumouredly)* Speak the Queen's tongue, man. You're as bad as my brother.

(He dismantles the horse's hooves)

SIR TARNASH. By mountain and glen, by burn and fen, we will be with you, Child Roland, till journey's end.

ROLAND. Rise up, Sir Tarnash. You are my trusted squire.

SIR TARNASH. On, Prince! As we go, we will study the features of this grim old landscape, and pass the time courteously and well.

ROLAND. *(Graciously)* I'm sure we will, old fellow.

ISLA. And I will cook and sew and -

COWIE. And I will nick the kindling stick from Nicky-ben himself to warm you, Lord Roland!

SIR TARNASH. Well said, well said -

*(They go.
The light goes)*

Scene Two - The Plain

(ROLAND and SIR TARNASH enter wearily. ISLA and COWIE bring up the rear. They drop their loads and sit huddled together.)

ROLAND. We have gone a hundred leagues, Sir Tarnash.

COWIE. Let us rest here, master. I will get stick and kindle a fire for Isla to cook soup and beans for us.

SIR TARNASH. *(sharply)* We cannot rest here. We have to find the hateful cripple who will point the way.

ROLAND. It is a level plain all round. There is no path to tell. Only the dead tree there.

SIR TARNASH. Look again. *(ROLAND moves to look)*

ROLAND. The cripple!

SIR TARNASH. Seize him!

(COWIE grasps the thin bent man and brings him to ROLAND)

SIR TARNASH. Tell my Lord Roland the road to Elfland,
Cripple! You cannot choose but tell all wayfarers. You stand
there to waylay them with lies, to ensnare all travellers are you
posted here, but we will tear the truth from your throat!

(CRIPPLE laughs and shakes his staff at them)

COWIE. Tell thy tale! *(Winks at CRIPPLE)* I'll gie ye a drap
of guid ale.

ISLA. Let the body speak, if it's in its power.

SIR TARNASH. It will pour out evil council. Yet we must hear.

CRIPPLE. *(Reasonably)* I shall discuss this matter with you.
You must come to my house, which lies embosomed in a grove
of trees.

ROLAND. No trees do I see to the furthest sky where the sun
is setting.

CRIPPLE. Along the sweet water side, passing through graceful
walks and between trimly kept hedges, Child Roland and Sir
Tarnash, you will soothe the dull cold ear of death. Back to its
mansion call the fleeting breath.

ROLAND. No, I shan't. I may not trust you. I decline your
doubtful offer.

CRIPPLE. *(Cringingly)* Your honour, it's true, I am a snake in
the grass, a toad under a stone. I could not speak of things
with the likes of you. My words are low, you must not stoop.
In my narrow cell I am laid. The turf is above. It is a
mouldering heap. I heave under it like a worm.

(Falls and wriggles on the ground)

COWIE. I wadna gie him to the burds!

ISLA. Poor man - he's in a woeful plight.

(CRIPPLE leaps up like a pistol fired off)

CRIPPLE. I with the fairies got a fright, and after that was never right.

COWIE. Sair smitten!

ROLAND. Cripple, hateful as you are, and in league with the devil, you must tell us what you know, and set us on the dreadful tract, though we never return.

SIR TARNASH. *(Commandingly)* Point the road!

(CRIPPLE starts drawing with his staff in the dust)

ROLAND. *(Looks at what CRIPPLE has drawn)* That is not the road!

CRIPPLE. Nay, that is my pastime.

ISLA. What does he write, then?

CRIPPLE. Thy epitaph, Roland!

(COWIE pushes him over. The CRIPPLE kicks in the air like a weasel)

SIR TARNASH. Liar! Ten times scored liar!

CRIPPLE. *(Wags staff at him)* Go the way I point to thee, no gladness ever shall you see, nor joy at the end will be.

ROLAND. On the contrary, Cripple, Burd Ellen will be there, and my brothers twain, and my father dear, King of Scandanna, and good knights more to win from thrall. So therefore much joy at the end will be, and all will gain their happier lives again just as have these three companions of mine here. Now stop mucking about, and point the way!

(CRIPPLE scrambles to his feet. He points one way with his staff)

CRIPPLE. There, there! Wrang-Gaites Way is there!

SIR TARNASH. Take up your burdens!

(COWIE and ISLA shoulder their bags etc. and move off. SIR TARNASH touches ROLAND'S arm. ROLAND nods, and draws his sword)

ROLAND. You are right. First I must rid his neck of that evil mask.

CRIPPLE. Spare me, Lord Roland, a cripple man!

SIR TARNASH. Fool! Why do you cling to your malice?

ROLAND. I may make you a true man again. Durindal will free

your soul, however wicked.

CRIPPLE. Spare me!

SIR TARNASH. Come, Roland. He is too wicked for thee. What good to release from thrall such a spirit?

(They turn away. They take a pace or so. The CRIPPLE is a palsied tree again.

A grey screen hides the tree from view.

ROLAND turns)

ROLAND. Look, Sir Tarnash, look! The road has gone - the highway has utterly gone! There is nothing but greyness to the horizons bound! Sir Tarnash! There is no way back now!

SIR TARNASH. *(Grimly)* We go on. Nought else remains to do.

(They go on)

Scene Three - The Forest

(The greyness becomes a greenness. The dense hue shelters shadowy creatures . . . . The travellers settle for the night. ISLA forages. She has a hold-all. She pops things in. This is her forte. But on this occasion her scrounging proves nearly fatal. She pops the bright berries in the bag)

ISLA. That will taste nicely with the rest.

COWIE. *(Gathers sticks)* What have ye for the pot, Isla? the bag is heavy. Ach, ye'd be a death-blow to a packman.

ISLA. *(Contentedly)* I like to stow things away. *(Finds more fruit and nuts)*

COWIE. The things you've got in here! Bawbees, napkins, cocky wigs, seals -

ISLA. *(Complacently)* Waste not, want not. Things come in handy, don't they Cowie?

COWIE. Brave scrounging! *(Lights fire. ISLA prepares pot)* Between you and me, Henwife Isla, the forest is no place for it! What's here but cockle, spurge and tansie, fireweed and stinking willie?

(They sit by the fire.
ISLA tends the pot, popping herbs in.
SIR TARNASH stands on guard.
ROLAND stretches out to sleep)

SIR TARNASH. The Last Judgement's Fire must cure this place. I never saw such starved ignoble nature.

ROLAND. It's better than the plain. Here are green things growing. The grass grew scant and ragged on the Heath.

SIR TARNASH. Poisonous place! I feel ill at ease here. I would go forward. We might clear this scene of my fear. We might come to better country with hawthorn and may and water clear.

ROLAND. And we might not, Squire. Sleep, Sir Tarnash. Rest we will a little time.

ISLA. I have soup ready now!

(COWIE sits with ISLA. SIR TARNASH declines the soup.-
continues his watch)

COWIE. *(Drinks soup)* My ain fireside, my ain fireside, O sweet is the blink of my ain fireside.

ISLA. *(Offers soup)* You will sleep better, Roland Chick.

ROLAND. I must not eat. I must only think of the morrow. I must listen to the echoes of the morn.

ISLA. *(Chattily)* Your golden slug-horn will you blow when the heathcock wakens, and the chant of the lark.

(Eats soup)

SIR TARNASH. We shall not hear that. We are more strange to this than we thought. Oh, for the rich fields of grain, and the chase on the mountain! Lord Roland, you have restored my dear thoughts to me. I have lived among Scotland's favoured sons.

ROLAND. Good. Now I'm going to sleep.

(He covers himself with his cloak. His sword is under his
head. His horn is under his cloak. His arm is over his cloak
and the glitter of his rings attracts the eye of ISLA)

COWIE. One taste of the old-time. *(Drinks from flask)* Sets

me to rights, that does. *(Curls up for sleep. ISLA looks at
the ring on ROLAND's finger flashing in the firelight. She
can't resist it. She pops it in her bag . . . she settles herself
for sleep. SIR TARNASH remains on guard.
Stage darkens. Scrim is lit. Figures and shapes come forth.
COWIE cries out. ISLA groans.
COWIE breathes stertorously, then lies still. ISLA croaks.
Silence. ROLAND sleeps profoundly.
MERLIN enters D.C. Lights come up on him. He is in his
wizard rig. D.L. is a stool and a table with magical apparatus.
He sits before the machinery, propping a book against it. It is
entitled 'How To Get Into People's Dreams'.*

MERLIN. Yes, yes! This forge has been burning night and day
for seven years. My patience is about to be rewarded. I am to
enter Prince Roland's dreams. By this means I may help him.
(Agitatedly) Two of his companions have been poisoned! I
must lose no time.

(He clasps his book. His beard flows over it)

I devote the last of my ancient wits to this task.

*(The dream which ROLAND is having begins to develop its
location upstage. The scrim may be raised.
ROLAND smiles in his dream.
The closet in the Tower where the fair BURD ELLEN has been
confined is revealed. Music for this. A couch. A dressing-
table with lots of potions on it. A mirror-mirror, that sort of
thing. Caged bird effect with sugary pink and golden twiddly
bits. BURD ELLEN has a long thin golden chain round her
waist. She has wound it rather attractively, but it is still a
nasty chain, as shall appear. And the potion bottles and sprays
will be of importance.
All this ROLAND is dreaming. A prescient and substantial
vision. MERLIN is racking his old brain to get into it.
ELLEN sits brushing her golden hair before the mirror-mirror in
the accustomed manner. There is a dreaminess about her. She
is only firing on about one cylinder.*

Music for the dungeons, to which ROLAND has turned his attention.

The brothers twain are crouching in the dank depths, their chains clanking illustratively when either moves in fitful sleep. They are manacled to posts. They are heavily and awfully enchanted. The ELF KING does not need them to play with like he does his canary bird.

ROLAND starts in his sleep.

Music for approach of terrifying KING OF ELFLAND.

ROLAND throws up an arm in mimic defence of ELLEN.

The brothers twain shudder in their enchantment. Their eyes are sightless and their ears are stopped. They just shudder awfully.

The warlock MERLIN downstage sees the scene - he watches - he can see - he can't get in yet.

MERLIN. I can see, I can't get in yet.

The poisoned COWIE and ISLA groan and croak.

SIR TARNASH kneels to minister to them.)

MERLIN. If I could get in, I could pass the antidote to Sir Tarnash. I can see it on the dressing-table. The Elf King has supplied his captive with this to show off and to keep her awake. Any of the poisons in which Wrang-Gaites Forest abounds may be dispersed in a trice by antidote sprays. But I just can't get at them. I must, I must! Roland needs the Cow-Herd and the Hen-Wife. He and Sir Tarnash alone will be too heroic. They need their rude companions, if they are to rescue the fair Burd Ellen and the Brothers Twain - to say nothing of the Good Old King and the various other casualties of honour. Wonder where the Elf King keeps them all. . . . Well, well. One thing at a time. If I could just get into Roland's dream! That'd be a starter.

(Music of approaching ELF KING. Dinosaur noises.

ELLEN stands to face her fearsome visitor, who bursts in . . . He is very large, frightful and gorgeous. The ELF KING is rather animal. He roars and rumbles. Sometimes he skips

*and giggles in an elephantine way. His style is strictly
dinosaurian. For example, when injured (as will occur later),
he has to stop and work out where he's been hit. He is quite
huge and fat with a big nose and fleshy lips. His skin has the
mortuary colour of a flesh-eater. He wears a vast long auburn
coloured beard, bushy eyebrows, ermine robes, and green and
blue fleur de lys on his trailing royal gown. But his royal
garments do not lessen the rhino style of movement and thought
processes. (Ter biff or not ter biff).*

*ELLEN, even if she is only firing on one cylinder, can still
fool him to the top of his bent. This is in fact the only way to
deal with him. She is completely confident although of course
within his power physically. She has the confidence of a
tightrope walker. But she is sleep-walking (So the actress
must make what she can of that)*

A dreamy wraithlike cheekiness.)

ELF KING. Are ye keepin' quiet, then, my canary? Ho ho. I've
come to play with my little bird.
*(ELLEN unwinds the golden chain from her waist - she skips
round him, flicking the fat lumbering playmate.)*
Ye flick me! Ho ho! Ye'll do nothing more. *(Lunges and
misses)* Hang it! *(Flops on sofa)* I'll have ye in a minute, my
little bird. Ye are outnumbered. Dinna ye fear ye will be
slain? Ye are very pert.

ELLEN. Are my cousins slain? *(Flicks him)*

ELF KING. Eek! Stop flicking me! Hang 'em, they're out
shooting on my grouse-moors. And they want you to marry me.
Her her. For the shooting. *(Catches chain, puts it in his
teeth)* Now, now, my Canary Princess - dance! Dance!
(ELLEN dances on her chain) Pretty! Pretty! Pretty toy!
Ho ho! I'll 'ave yer for my dinner! No, I won't, then. I
ain't goin' to eat you. I'm goin' to keep you for my toy! Yer
cousins give you to me for my joy!

ELLEN. You lie. You have chained them to posts.

ELF KING. Yeah. Mebbe I have. Mebbe I've eaten them. I

don't remember. *(Roaring)* No man shall presume to come
into my kingdom, though he be compelled by storm and grind,
the measure is meet, he is mine perpetually! Her her her.
This is the law. Haw haw haw. Flitting and flashing my spies
tell all. They lurk and listen at every turn of the trail and reek
of the land. Roland the Youngest will not escape.

ELLEN. *(Breaks from the EEK)* Where is Roland?

ELF KING. In the Petrified Forest. Why? That's two questions
too many you've asked me, you juicy canary. *(Lollops after
her. She sits on the sofa. He sits beside her, mooncalf like)*
Dicky ticky, little bird, do you like my whiskers? Her her her.
Do you like my face? Haw haw haw. *(Roars)* I am a man of
a hundred thousand, chieftain fell! Clang and bong and battle
stout with weapons flying, foot and horse, if you won't play my
games with me, I'll make you the main course.

ELLEN. I - I am faint. I need water.

ELF KING. Eek! Like to see some magic? *(Bellows in the
mirror)* Water! Water bring - from the nearest spring!
(Music - watery sounds)
It won't be long. I may decide to eat you. Aery female, pert
quiney, plaything for kings!

ELLEN. You are fat and clumsy.

ELF KING. Take care - I'll put you on a great spell - I didn't
yet - you shall lose these saving potions - *(Sweeps several
pots onto the floor)* - the air of the Tower will close and choke
your life - Ah! Little pretty! *(Makes to dance with her again)*

ELLEN. I crave, Lord of Elfland - you must dance no more.
How puffed you are!

ELF KING. Hee hee.

ELLEN. Now I drink at the stream. *(Stoops to drink)*

ELF KING. Hee hee. My Stream. I'm puffed.
(Closes eyes - sinks into sleep on sofa, ELLEN soothing him)

ELLEN. I this burning thirst may cool with water from the
foulest pool.
(Sprays ELF KING with potion. He is doggo on the sofa.)

Now his voice is grown so weak
Convulse him that he never speak!
(MERLIN runs in)

MERLIN. Done it! I've done it!

ELLEN. *(Weeps with relief)* Oh Merlin - what a hole I'm in.
How did you get here?

MERLIN. I came by dream boat from Grampia! There is not a
moment to spare. I am in Roland's dream with you. Soon he
may wake. Or the Elf King may wake inside the dream and kill
me with one biff.

ELLEN. Can't you use your magic? You must have some.
Get me out of this.

MERLIN. Impossible. Only Roland can rescue you. This is
just a flying visit. I can't stop to explain. You've got a
potion there - do you mind? - *(Rummages at dressing-table)* -
Yes, this one will do -

ELLEN. Is he coming?

MERLIN. He's got as far as the Forest. He's having this
dream there now. We're both in it. How are you managing, my
dear? Not treating you too badly?

ELLEN. He keeps me as a plaything. The Princes of
Scandanna are in dungeons drear, though he lies, and says they
are out shooting.

MERLIN. He is the Prince of Liars. I must get back before
Roland wakes. Don't worry about anything. I still have some
magic, old as I am. I can see Roland and his companions, for
instance. There they are! I want this potion because two of
them, Henwife Isla and Cowherd Cowie are like to die from the
poisoned berries of the Petrified Forest. How to get in - that's
the devil - if I could only get into the Forest too!

ELLEN. Still, getting into Roland's dream - that was something.
(Puts head on MERLIN's shoulder) I am so sad and drear,
though.

MERLIN. Bear up! You are yet blooming and fair. Excessively
fair, I should say.

ELLEN. I don't think about it. I'm heavily sedated. What
does Roland look like?

MERLIN. He smiles in his sleep to think of you. He looks
pale and interesting. He must bite no bit and drink no drop
till he gets to you, as you know . . . . Goodness, he's waking!
The croaking of the poisoned pair has aroused him. I must
hasten. Oh, I can see - but I cannot reach. Oh, he will end
his dream in a few seconds! If I could just get this antidote
to Sir Tarnash -

ELLEN. Where is he?

MERLIN. *(Pointing wildly)* There - just there!

ELLEN. *(Bored)* Give it to him, then.

MERLIN. A broad bartizan bars the way, a great curtain of gum
- I can't describe it!

ELLEN. Can't you lob the thing across?

MERLIN. I'll try!

*(Throws potion bottle. It rolls at SIR TARNASH's feet. He
picks it up and looks at it curiously)*

SIR TARNASH. Heavenly manna! Lord Roland awakes!
What can this mean?

MERLIN. Ellen - I can't get back - it's too late - I could only
have got back through the dream - I've left it too late!

ELLEN. We'll hide you in a cupboard.

MERLIN. Trapped in the Tower! Trapped in Elfland! What a
thing to happen to a respectable magician! What about the
affairs of Grampia? What about the business of good
government? Oh what a mess!

ELLEN. Two heads are better than one. And mine's only half
a head at the moment, if that. And you are a warlock. I need
all the help I can get against that - rhinoceros!

(ROLAND finally wakes.

The Dream figures (ELLEN, MERLIN, ELF KING) fade from view.
(ELLEN and MERLIN can wheel the EEK out on the sofa)

SIR TARNASH. Roland! Our companions are in desperate case.
I fear they are poisoned.

ROLAND. I have had such a dream! I was a fly on the wall of
the Closet in which the King of Elfland keeps Burd Ellen.
She has a golden chain around her waist and he can make her
dance on the end of this chain and he has foolish small pig
eyes and a huge nose. But Burd Ellen fools him to the top of
his bent. He was snoring on the sofa. Oh - and Merlin came
and picked up a pot of something - I can't say what - I can't
say how he got into my dream either, but he did, and I wasn't
dreaming it, was I? - oh well . . . . anyway, he told me about
my poisoned companions - and he threw the antidote to you out
of the dream, so do use it, for goodness sake!

SIR TARNASH. Yes, yes I have it here! *(Steadies the groaning
COWIE, and splashes the potion on his face)* May the potion
be the right one!

ROLAND. What a dream I have had!

SIR TARNASH. He is coming to!

(Curious, ROLAND watches COWIE's contorted recovery)

ROLAND. One might have to drink it. It's more usual.

SIR TARNASH. Isla, stay still. Will you drink?

ISLA. *(Spluttering)* Where are we? What ails you, Sir Tarnash?
How green you are!

ROLAND. The Forest is where we are, where everything is
venomous and green, slimey green - and you have been a silly
Isla, and fed poisoned berries to Cowie and yourself.

SIR TARNASH. *(Banging COWIE on the back)* Do you feel your
body back again, Cowie?

COWIE. Oh Sir Tarnash, ye have saved my skin, in all
likelihood.

ISLA. Away with the berries, then! *(Tips out her hold-all.
Roland's ring falls out)* Oh!

ROLAND. Why have you my ring from my finger, Isla?

SIR TARNASH. She is a false traitress to her prince!
(Wrathful descent)

ISLA. *(Wails)* I am a displeasing body - I can't help picking
and stealing - woe is me!

COWIE. *(Disgustedly)* Gae to Hecklebirnie!

SIR TARNASH. She is constrained in her conscience. We may
spare her.

(ISLA sniffles)

ROLAND. Our present condition, my good companions, admits
of no delay in petty dispute.

SIR TARNASH. *(To ISLA)* Cease thy clatter!

ROLAND. Gather up the bags, Cowie. Isla, help him. Sir
Tarnash, we must march towards the dawn.

COWIE. Which way's that?

SIR TARNASH. We must clear this foul Forest!

(They go)

Scene Four. - The Up-and-Down Place.

(The companions emerge from the forest.
It is dawn.
The prospects are fair.)

SIR TARNASH. What penned us in that wicked Forest, with all
the plain to choose? Look, Roland - broad pastures open up
before.

ISLA. There are birds singing!

SIR TARNASH. Rich groves of stately trees - towards which
spins a fine road. Oh Roland, are you not gratified by such a
sight?

COWIE. We mun not be hasty, Sir Tarnash. Tis not the straight
road - but bears away from us, like a sign of repentance.

ROLAND. We have now arrived at a kind of fork in the way, and
one goes up and one goes down, not a pace from the Forest.
Cowie is right. We should take some care. We shall be
getting off the path, you know.

SIR TARNASH. Such is the appearance. My instincts prevent
all fear. Let me go ahead to test the ground, Roland. You
will see what speed I shall make in that grand extensive way.

I long to breathe the air there, for I know it will be sweet.
Rest here while I advance!

ROLAND. On this quernstone we'll sit.

*(They sit. SIR TARNASH goes on U.S. and out of our sight.
He sings as he goes)*

SIR TARNASH. *(Singing)* Nor shall thy guidance but conduct
our feet, through all the splendid labyrinths of heaven! . . . .
Oh what power in the weary limbs of a knight! Believe me,
I am gently led!

(His voice fades.

Pause.

*COWIE stretches against the quernstone in the morning sun.
The light is lambent.)*

COWIE. Och! I ache! Upon my guts, ye have near murdered
me, Isla, with your snowberries.

ISLA. *(Indignantly)* No such thing! It was the wicket Forest
deceiving a guidwife.

ROLAND. All on Wrang-Gaites Way give wicked council, Isla.
Prayer cannot prevail. All is deceiving, lies and death.

(SIR TARNASH's voice crying out)

SIR TARNASH. Help! Help!

(They run U.S.)

COWIE. He has fallen in a bog!

SIR TARNASH. *(O/S)* I am drowning! Save yourself, Roland!
Come not near me. All is deceiving. The Broad Pastures is
but a filthy bog. I am drowned! I am drowned!

ROLAND. Pull ivy from the trees at the Forest edge. Quickly,
Cowie.

(They run back)

ISLA. *(Shouts)* Hold your nose, noble Sir Tarnash! We will
save you. They are bringing ivy strands to fling across the
bog!

SIR TARNASH. Help! Help!

*(ROLAND and COWIE pull ivy creeper on - long twisted cords
of it)*

COWIE. Wicket stuff, like snakes it is. *(Pulls U/S)*

ISLA. *(Screams)* It is snakes!

COWIE. *(Roars)* I'm coming, Knight! *(Goes U/S with snaky creepers)*

ROLAND. *(Takes other end, which wriggles and twists)* Living venom, hold still! *(Lashes head of creeper with his sword. It is still. ISLA prods dead head.)*

ISLA. It was. Ugh. It was a snake.
(They pull SIR TARNASH from the bog. He is all covered with leeches.)

SIR TARNASH. *(Groans)* I am dead! I am dead!

COWIE. *(Comes to look at him)* Ugh! *(Staggers back from horrid sight)* They've sucken Sir Tarnash to death! Forty days victual for a pack o' leeches!
(ISLA fetches powder from hold-all. Sprinkles the trembling knight)

ISLA. This will serve. I keep it handy. What a sight you are, Sir Tarnash. Keep still, Knight. There's six of 'em done for. *(Knocks leeches off)*

COWIE. *(Sweeping up behind her and throwing leeches into the audience)* Quivering bleedy fray - sair to save, ye are. It should have been thy death-note.

SIR TARNASH. *(Weakly)* Thanks, dear friends. O Prince, thou hast rescued me.

ROLAND. Cowie and Isla have saved your life, Sir Tarnash . . Now we know our way to go.
(Points D/S. They peer D/S)
It is not a pleasant prospect, I grant you, my tired companions. The way descends at once to a black glen, with a black burn at the foot of it.

COWIE. Tis a slithery stinkin' brae. Bodoch-na-dun! - Tis the very ghost of a hill.

ROLAND. Now we shall descend it.

ISLA. It is covered with stones which clack and slither all ways. We will be dashed to the bottom! Our feet will never hold up,

Roland Chick.

ROLAND. *(Cheerily)* Down you go, Mother Isla!

ISLA. We're doomed for sure to part.

(ROLAND goes first with ISLA, and COWIE follows with SIR TARNASH.)

SIR TARNASH. Cowie! We must not hold back!

(QUEEN MOTHER appears in a spot)

QUEEN MOTHER. I'm in a spot. There is still no sign of my Court Chamberlain, Merlin Caledonius. I have sent to his cave. No trace of the old warlock appears. My servants have searched in all the retorts and curious engines which work ceaselessly night and day in his primitive establishment of dubious renown, to no avail. He has gone and changed himself into a mouse or something ridiculous and can't get back into shape. He's a bit past it. Anyway, I really can't have this! So I am putting out a decree. Unfortunately he isn't here to promulgate it for me. Oh well, I shall have to do it myself, I suppose. *(Reads from scroll of knitting)* No one is allowed to go off on any chivalric or necromantic expeditions whatsoever. The depopulation of Grampian ruling circles is becoming a national scandal! *(Spot fades. Voice fades)* So I'm just not having it any longer . . . . .

Scene Five - The Burn.

(The good companions slither in, head over tails, stones flying. They pick themselves up.

An OLD WOMAN is looking at them, arms akimbo)

COWIE. *(Dusts himself down)* Hullo, Grannie. What place is this then?

OLD WOMAN. Let it suffice to advert to the sign on yonder bridge, ye peelie-wally keelie-wappit!

ROLAND. *(Reads sign)* 'Burning Bones Hotel. Views of the Devil's Elbow. Teas on the Terrace above the sepulchral

Field'.

COWIE. *(Looks over bridge)* I see the Devil's Beard, and a water-rat is tangled in it. *(Shriek splits the air)*

ISLA. Good saints!

OLD WOMAN. Well, well. Tak' care if ye ford the stream, for ye may set foot upon a dead man's cheek. *(Cackles)*

SIR TARNASH. *(Looks over)* The eddies are so black!

COWIE. All bespate with flakes and spumes!

ROLAND. So petty yet so spiteful!

OLD WOMAN. Aye. Sometimes it sounds like a baby's shriek, sometimes like toads in a poisoned tank, or wild cats in a red hot cage!

(Assorted illustrative cries from below)

ROLAND. We must cross, at all events.

OLD WOMAN. Ye can but try. *(Watches with interest.)*

(ROLAND goes halfway across - the others hang back.
Tentacles reach towards him over the side of the narrow plank walk.

Music of Monsters.

ROLAND cuts at the tentacles with Durindal.

COWIE and SIR TARNASH go to back him up.

They are driven back by spiders or something.

Confusion. Cries. Crashes. Black-outs. Splashes.
Flying limbs. ROLAND is wounded but fights on. The OLD
WOMAN dances on the far bank, having jumped nimbly across.)

OLD WOMAN. Now at 'em - over there! - ow, you devil! The monster reels men's bodies out like silk. Ow! he bleeds! . . . Off he goes again. Bog clay and nibble! Sand and stark black dearth! Look at that, then! Hee hee hee.

ROLAND. *(In the thick of it)* Just merit for thee, monstrous pains! *(Cuts and hacks)* Devils, monsters, all extinguished be in deep, dark flood!

(The monsters subside. OLD WOMAN runs out.

There are sweeter strains heard.

SIR TARNASH and COWIE cross the plank and carry ROLAND

to the far bank. ISLA scampers over too. She bathes his
wounds with salve from her hold-all
The OLD WOMAN comes back in with laden tray of sweetmeats
and little cakes, wine and fruit etc.)

OLD WOMAN. The best of my cupboard and cellar are yours, weary travellers. Sigh no more nor weep. The Prince is brave. He lives. Those fishy monsters could not wrap his clay. I'm his hieland grannie, I know what I am saying! I have an uncertain trade, as you may imagine, sirs, cheek a-jowl with all nature's deadliest foes. I welcome openly so happy a band.

ISLA. Ooh, what things you've found us, grannie.

SIR TARNASH. It will be time for breakfast, I doubt not.

COWIE. Warms your heart!

(They set to. ROLAND raises himself on one elbow)

OLD WOMAN. Will the Brave Prince no eat? *(Holds food and drink towards ROLAND. He stares at it, puzzled)*

ROLAND. Faint I am. My strength ebbs.

OLD WOMAN. Eat! Drink!

ROLAND. Shall I?

OLD WOMAN. It's your hieland grannie's cakes!

ROLAND. *(To audience)* Shall I? *(Audience advises him)*

OLD WOMAN. I'll pay you off for that! *(Bares dentures at audience)* Eat! Drink! Your companions are tucking in to grannie's nice hieland slobbits and peckits, and the water of life is flowing back into their peelie-wally veins!

ROLAND. Shall I? Shall I eat? *(Audience advises him)*

OLD WOMAN. Ooh, I'll breech you - I'll tuck your kilts over my knee!

ROLAND. Old woman, I'll not eat. In happier days, which will come, when my poor mite of chivalry I've paid and deedily have done, and only then, when Burd Ellen I have won, will I eat and drink. Begone, witch!

(He thrusts the OLD WOMAN away, and her tray falls into the torrent.)

OLD WOMAN. *(Screams)* I'll pay you off for that, Roland!
*(She runs at him, but trips over Durindal and falls into the
torrent herself. Eerie screams fade to silence. ROLAND
rises from the ground. SIR TARNASH and COWIE peer over
the side.)*

COWIE. The grannie's blood sprinkles the bank with red
flowerets.

SIR TARNASH. Grace of Mother Mary! *(Crosses himself)*

ROLAND. On we must go. One desperate effort, friends -
the last. See - the two hills on the right!

ISLA. We see them!

ROLAND. While, to the left, a tall scalped mountain!

COWIE. We see it!

ROLAND. Tis there! We must climb the Great Glack where in
the midst stands the Tower itself. It has no counterpart in
the whole world. We shall see it before the dying sunset
kindles through that cleft! Strike on!

Scene Six - The Glack.

*(Wind and tempest. Music of the spheres. Cannonades
of severe sound. Dark shapes and cries of owls, bats and the
like creatures of darkness. The stage is filled with necromantic influences as well as natural fury. Darkness covers the
earth. - and gross darkness the people. Clattering and banging,
discrepant uproars and contrapuntal outcry. Cacophony and
tintinnabulation. Hail and fire as a matter of course.
Enter ROLAND. SIR TARNASH, COWIE and ISLA stagger after
him past a bare rock face)*

SIR TARNASH. *(In the teeth of a ghastly gale)* This is the
Glenger Rock, a place to fear!

COWIE. Aye - and a place to pause! Sich a sloggan! Twudna'
hurt to rest a little.

ROLAND. Strike on! *(Goes U/S out of sight)*

ISLA. *(Shrieks)* Roland Chick! The roof of the world is blowing off!

SIR TARNASH. Tis fearful! But heart-blood burst before we gasp, and fall like lumps of clay!

ISLA. I'm too tired, Sir Tarnash! *(Sits down)*

SIR TARNASH. Rouse yourself, Isla! *(Pulls her up)*

COWIE. I'm butchered and houthered, I'm scal'd and sca'd, I'm scrunted and squished, I'm stushach'd and stun'd. And I can't go any further.

SIR TARNASH. Then you must go a long piece further!

(Drives them on U/S. We lose sight of them.

The tempest rages.

Flash of lightning illuminates the stage.

The shadows of great bird wings.

ROLAND comes D/C alone, Durindal held high.

He stands as though at the sheer face of a cliff.

He strikes Durindal three times against the cliff face.

He unslings his horn.)

ROLAND. I came! I came! Child Roland to the Dark Tower came! Open and let me come in!

(He blows his horn.

A grinding of great iron hinges, shrieking of rods, pranging and pronging, splitting and rending of geological formations.

A great cleft appears in the blackness.

A blazing light spinning round and round.

ROLAND blows his horn again - and again -

END OF ACT TWO

ACT THREE.

Scene One - Charm Closet (Dark Tower)

(ELLEN, MERLIN, EEK)
(EEK snores on sofa)

MERLIN. Time is passing. Oh bother. Not that time means
anything here, you know. All the same, Princess, we ought to
think about releasing the Brothers Twain from the dungeon
drear in which they are incarcerated - unless my inward eye
deceives me.

ELLEN. What bothers me is the Eek may wake up.

MERLIN. I am sure you will charm him to sleep again, my dear!

ELLEN. Can't think why.

MERLIN. Just keep puffing powder up his snout. I'd better
get along now, Princess. I cannot allow the High Prince of
Grampia to moulder away in that dungeon any longer.

ELLEN. I'm not staying here on my own! I simply haven't got
the strength to keep that beastly rhinoceros under.

MERLIN. We'll fix something up. A little ingenuity, Princess!
Your golden chain, please!

ELLEN. I don't know if I can get it off. It's been magicked.

MERLIN. *(Laughs heartily)* Then we'll just have to unmagick
it, won't we? *(Makes cabalistic signs at ELLEN's midriff)*
Your English waistline has dwindled sufficiently, perhaps,
under the severities of your imprisonment.

ELLEN. You are pompous, Caledonius! *(Wriggles out of chain)*
Still, you're not a bad old warlock, after all!
(Hangs chain round his neck)

MERLIN. Now to make adjustments with my clever old fingers.
(Fiddles with rhino hooves of EEK) This we slip on here -
and this here. *(Attaches to magic powder pot)* A trip
mechanism - so! If he stirs, he tugs the chain, and - Puff!
Off he goes again!

ELLEN.   Wizard arrangement!

MERLIN.   *(Straightening)* And now let us lose no time.   Though
time has lost its meaning, at any moment the golden horn will
sound - your heroic rescuer will be at hand!

ELLEN.   And he will ride in, and, without further ado, will kill
my fell captor, the nefarious Eek, the rhinoceros!

MERLIN.   Ye-es.   He won't in fact be on a horse.   But that is
the general effect, certainly.   Mind you, he hasn't had an easy
time of it!   He has overcome monsters, had hairbreadth escapes,
so on and so forth.   An appreciative greeting will be in order.

ELLEN.   What do you suggest?

MERLIN.   The young champion must be met by gentlest dame in
sweetest garb with transcendent grace and loveliest looks - put
on your bit of best for your rescuer, my dear.   I assure you it's
very necessary.

ELLEN.   O.K.   After we've released the Brothers Twain, I'll
hop back up to the charm closet and get into something dreamy.
Then I'll sit up in the casement window, for Roland to approach
me at.

MERLIN.   Fitting moment!

ELLEN.   No time for fittings!

(They go)

Scene Two - Dungeon Drear.

(Brothers Twain. Heavy sleep-in, perforce.
GAOLER, dozing on duty. He looks like COWIE's brother -
he is. ELLEN and MERLIN creep up. MERLIN, stooping to
enter murky place, loses his hat. Being a very tall conical
object, it falls with a clatter. GAOLER jumps but subsides)

ELLEN.   Ohh!   Don't DO that, Merlin!

MERLIN.   So sorry, Princess.   *(Retrieves cap shamefacedly)*

ELLEN.   Ooh, how horrid the warder looks!

MERLIN.   *(Peers at him)* Dear me, yes.   He was a decent

country soul, who had the misfortune to bite into a piece of
cheese, which was full of the little people. They carried him
off in a colander. He was very sea-sick. *(Adjusts hat)*
Sorry about this, I have to wear it, as I expect you know. It
has been mathematically designed to attract cosmic help, which
we may very well need.

(ELLEN kneels to look at the Brothers Twain)

ELLEN. They do look ill, don't they? Quickly to revive them!
Let's hope we've brought some suitable splosh. It's funny the
Eek leaving that sort of stuff around.

(MERLIN kneels to administer)

MERLIN. The Elf King is very stupid. He is about as stupid
as a man can be. He is not a man, of course, but we may
classify him very roughly as belonging to the sub-species
Homo Wallah Wallah. Such growlers do not distinguish at all
clearly between the necessary and the contingent. Ah - not
the right potion.

*(The Brothers Twain, from being curled forlornly enough in
deep comas, now stretch themselves in agonising sticklike
postures. MERLIN sits down to examine the contents of his
pockets - which he had, as we should have mentioned at the
time, fairly stuffed with potions out of the charm closet.)*

ELLEN. Do hurry, Merlin Caledonius. They've practically
stopped breathing now!

MERLIN. *(Examining labels)* Icecake. Red Wall. Star-map.
Blitz-Krieg. Orange-sock. Try this one. *(Showers liberally
The Brothers stir)* Orange-sock it is, by all my intractable
powers!

(The WARDER stirs too)

ELLEN. Oh dear, he's got a spin-off.

*(The WARDER staggers upright and circles the dungeon at top
speed with his eyes shut.)*

Give him a quick burst of that first thing! Give him a bit of
the first. Here - let me!

(Fires burst of icecake. PORTER does best fall since

Feuillere and lies still as any stone.

Goodness - that's the stuff to give prison warders all right!
*(The Brothers Twain are on their feet by now, eyes wide open.
But they are still very groggy)*

MERLIN.   They are yet deprived of speech.

ELLEN.   Poor things.   Shall we try something else?   Might be
pushing our luck a bit, I suppose.   Ooh, -look at those horrid
iron ring marks on High Prince George's legs.   Bruce has
partly chewed his through.   What a man . . . .   But Merlin, we
must unchain them!

MERLIN.   Such is our task.   The Warder will have the key.
(They search WARDER's bunch of keys)

ELLEN.   He's got hundreds!   There must be ever so many
dungeons - full of enchanted knights.

MERLIN.   *(Shakes head)*   Rotten business.   We will have to
go through them all.
*(They try to raise WARDER to get keys off him, but he is as
stiff as a stiff)*

ELLEN.   It's no good.   He weighs half a ton!

MERLIN.   We'll have to administer a slight reagent.

ELLEN.   Just enough to get him to sit up.

MERLIN.   'Pink Prickle' - Try this.   *(He administers it.
WARDER shudders, eases a little, more sack-like.   ELLEN
goes for his belt.   He giggles and rolls about as she touches
him)*

PORTER OF THE DARK TOWER.   Leave off, you baggage!
(The sound of ROLAND's horn, clear and near)

ELLEN.   He is here, he is here!   *(They rise hastily)*
(Pats Brothers Twain reassuringly)
Don't worry - we'll be back.   Don't go away!   I have to make
ready to greet my rescuer.
*(Trips out.
GEORGE and BRUCE look piteously after her.
MERLIN collects up potions)*

MERLIN.   Stuff them under the palliasse for us, will you,

Princes? No, you haven't got palliasses, have you? Stuff
them under the filthy rat-infested straw. These will be the
ve ry thing to put you to rights, as soon as I have a moment to
concentrate my powers a bit. Of course, they're all his
proprietory products - not my kind of thing at all. It will be
simplest in the long run for Prince Roland to cause the Elf King
to yield and beg for mercy. Then he'll just have to lift all
these proprietory spells of his, in order to be spared. Yes, that
the best thing really. So hang on, you dear honourable and
pitifully maltreated Princes - oops!

*(Hides - as PORTER surfaces from half-life to raging action-
stations. The horn sounds a second time.)*

PORTER. Burning batches of pronged prisoners! Stenches
of sarcophagi and hot chinese tortures! I won't have it!
(Seizes pranging fork. Prods the Princes viciously)
Back, back! Back into your bad beds of rat-infested straw!
How dare you look so lively? I'll bend you permanently in a
minute. I've just got to see what that perishing hornblower
thinks he's playing at, waking the dead o' the Dark Tower.
I'll teach him another tune!

(He rushes out.

*Brothers Twain hug each other despite clankers. Dance
dreefully.*

MERLIN shakes his head and slips away)

Scene Three - The Hall.

(PORTER runs in

There is hammering at the portal)

PORTER. What's this, what's this? What mice are nibbling
at the lid of the morning? Muffle your bird-feet! Doze on!
Take your noses from the wall! I'm not bothered. I stay put
according to habit.

(Sits against portal)

You won't budge me an inch. I never yet opened that black
rock to no twig fingers pushing holes in the night sky!

SIR TARNASH. *(Off)* From stone to cloud we have ascended.
Shall we rest a finger's length from the goal?

PORTER. As to that, Sir Voice, I can't rightly say. You could
try folding up on a pane of ice. You could try skidding in the
scree where the herby people slop us out. I'm blank-brained
as water to thy silly cries, Sir Voice.

COWIE. *(Off)* I know that voice!

PORTER. I know that voice. But I'm not shifting in a hurry.
I rest my back against the well of the world. I am green and
indifferent. Claw at the grey wall, no life is in this, only
sourness - so wheel off! Swivel your heads! Your cries
escape like steam out of mouth-holes. Can't you stop it? I'm
Porter of the Dark Tower, I'm not in this for peanuts! And I'm
not Inspector of Nocturnal Nuisances either!

(The horn blows one last time, long and clear.

The portal opens of its own accord.

The PORTER staggers back)

Ooh, that's a mean trick!

(ROLAND enters the Dark Tower, Durindal raised high.

The Knight SIR TARNASH, COWIE and ISLA enter behind him)

ROLAND. *(Heroically)* I have not forgotten thee, dear dead
souls! I have come, I have come! Child Roland to the Dark
Tower came! I have crossed the barren heath and the bald
plain, I have tracked through the dismal Forest, and over the
river of dead men's bones with my chosen companions.
Brothers Twain, my deeds will earn thy souls their joy. My
father, I have brought your brand that never struck in vain, and
I will stab and end the creature - that eldritch King that
enthralls your soul! Then, father of heroes, I will give thy
brand to the eddying winds, which alone will remember these
mighty deeds! *(Hasty afterthought)* But not before I have
likewise restored from crooked thrall Avalon's most beautiful
and intelligent daughter, the fair Burd Ellen!

COWIE. Aye. Wouldn't do to forget her, master. But never mind the glittering words. There's a monster and a half here! Hullo, Mickey! Don't you remember your big brother? And aren't you ashamed of yourself, looking like a fat pig with poisoned bristles? Settle your fat-pig face, little brother, and give us the freedom of Elfland!

ISLA. He's never your brother, Cowie!

COWIE. My younger brother it is!

PORTER. Tis Jimmy an a'!

COWIE. He used to stretch by my side in the big bed. And now he only knows to bristle like a stupid fat pig-boar that doesn't know its own strength.

SIR TARNASH Stand aside, Porter of the Dark Tower, or we the floor with thy crimson blood perforce must strew. Throw down at once all locks keys and chains of dungeons drear. Pray for the mercy the heavens may use on you!

ISLA. He doesn't look like praying, Sir Tarnash.

(Enter above on her balcony or casement or whatever the fair BURD ELLEN. She maybe is unveiled like a fairy monument. Do what you like, but make her look good. Because she is good, as well as intelligent. However at present she is involved in an almost royal performance and is a bit deeved with it and you had better all pay attention.
Music of massed faery choirs.

ROLAND doesn't see her at first but SIR TARNASH does and ISLA too gapes. ROLAND has Durindal held aloft, and is really waiting to complete his own entrance effectively. He is wondering whether he should lop the ravening PORTER who is bestially bouncing and snorting and generally making a nuisance of himself and rushing at the intruders like a puzzled pig.)

COWIE. *(Wrestles with him)* Ducks and geese - wally wally! Whoah there! - no good lopping this one, Lord Roland. Smack in the piggy eye, that's more the thing!

(Knocks PORTER out cold)

ROLAND. Thanks, Cowie. *(Puts up Durindal, laughing)* Your

Roland is trying to rescue Bird Elbn from the Elf king in battle

fist was better.

(Sees ELLEN.

Falls on his knee.)

Oh Ellen! Burd Ellen! Brawling, we saw you not. You in
liquid beauty sparkling, we disregarded in unsightly manoeuvres
with this tedious porter of the Dark Tower. You in blue depths
unsleeping -

(Makes to approach her but she gestures him back sombrely)

ELLEN. Yes, that's all very nice, but I'm under a spell. You've
done nothing about that yet. You won't break the spell of the
eerie idiot with a lot of speeches. This is where the action is!
(More languidly) I am under the sea, I am over the edge of time.
You must not touch me. I cannot give you any help either.
(Afterthought) Still, I'm glad you get the general idea, and are
not too conceited.

(MONSTERS come in

*ROLAND has his back to them - continues to pay his knightly
respects to the Princess ELLEN above - while his companions
below have a bad time of it.*

*Without a sound, Monsters pin themselves yukkily if not slimily
to the good companions. SIR TARNASH and COWIE take them
on - ISLA lays about her with her hold-all. They give a
desperate account of themselves. It's a silent, slow-motion
encounter, nightmarish enough. The Monsters wrap themselves
around them. They use things and thongs and it is quite a
nasty do. Lasts up to two minutes. In the upshot the brave
companions and the yukky monsters are equally exhausted and
lie about the hall.*

Dinosaur Music. Thunder and sulphur light.

EEK bursts in. He wears a great horn helmet.

Stands snorting and stamping.

ELLEN cries out. MERLIN enters.

ROLAND turns.

Faces EEK. Draws Durindal)

EEK. Ter biff - or not ter biff? Ter biff - or not ter -

ROLAND. Have at thee!

EEK. Gercher! Err! Gerrrrrr!!

(Contest begins. EEK charges in straight lines with horn and brand. ROLAND has to move mighty fast. There are these monsters to trip him.

MERLIN umpires badly, getting in the way. The business is half funny and half horrid. MERLIN's gown caught up in EEK's horn. But ROLAND is in deadly earnest and so is the EEK)

EEK. *(In brief pause)* Fee fi fo fum!

ROLAND. Strike, Bogle!

EEK. I'll dash your brains from your brain pan!

ROLAND. If thou darest!

(But after all, ROLAND cannot fail. He beats the King of Elfland to the ground. He stands over him, his sword point at his throat. ELLEN now comes grandly down and prods the prostrate EEK with her pink satin toe)

ELLEN. Take his horn off!

EEK. Mercy!

ELLEN. I wonder what other bits come off this blustering fat man.

MERLIN. *(From safe distance)* Stay your hand, Roland! He must release all who are captive here, he must lift all his spells. You mustn't attempt to dismantle him before he's done that. You're not free either yet, Princess. Do be careful.

ROLAND. Elf King, do you yield?

EEK. I yield, I yield! I beg for mercy!

ROLAND. I grant thee mercy. Release Burd Ellen from thy spells and raise my noble father and my brothers to life, and let us all go free, and thou shalt be spared.

EEK. I agree.

(The flattened mound that was the EEK rises from the ground and divests itself of borrowed animal glory. What emerges is not without dignity - the tawny haired, hooknose ruin shambles past ROLAND and fumbles in a chest. From the chest he takes a phial filled with blood-red liquor. With this he anoints

the eyes of BURD ELLEN, her eyelids, nostrils, lips and
finger-tips)

ELF KING. Thy soul has been away, Princess. Now it returns.

ROLAND. Now what about my brothers?

ELF KING. I will pronounce a general dismissal of devils, and
drivels, incubi and succubi, cramps and little prating scamps.

MERLIN. Yes, yes - that will do!

ELLEN. Funny, I don't feel all that different.

MERLIN. Spells have their own dynamism.

ELF KING.   The way the hands of the clock move
                Little black things below and above
                Come here you and take your reel
                Guess what I mean. The word is DEISEAL!

ECHOES. Deiseal! Deiseal! Deiseal!

MERLIN. Extraordinary. I used to know things like that.

ELF KING. What more, Childe Roland?

ROLAND. I see no brothers or yet my noble father.

ELLEN. Do you know what he looks like? I thought he left
when you were tiny.

ROLAND. His features are engraved on my heart. I've also
got a cameo - but I left that at home. Goodness, Princess
Ellen, that's no problem.

ELF KING. It may be. They have all been released but will
have to make their own ways home. They have already left.

ELLEN. That's rubbish - they were in your dungeon, you
ruined wraith - Merlin and I were with them a minute ago.

MERLIN. Time has no meaning here, Princess - I keep telling
you. And I shouldn't argue the toss - even with a ruined
wraith. As a matter of fact he remains, for all Lord Roland's
great victory over evil, a very formidable force with which we
are dealing. The sooner we take our departure the better.

ELF KING. Yes, I have many tones of voice, and many life
styles, and though it may take a century or two to get back
into trim, I am definitely still in business. There is still

nastiness, wickedness, lies and cruelty.   There is still plenty
to work on - isn't there?

(Thunder and sulphurous light.

The ELF KING is gone)

MERLIN.   Masterly - you've got to hand it to him.

*(And now the companions of honour and the monsters all arise
and dance.   And all their yukky bits fall off the monsters and
are kicked away.   They are all people again.*

Dance of monsters and good companions)

Scene Four - Palace Garden of Grampia.

*(The QUEEN, in royal basket chair, knitting or weaving a
tapestry, or crocheting if preferred.*

*The scene may be played before the curtain while the throne
room is being set.)*

QUEEN.   Voices of my lost sons are with me, wherever I go.
I have reached the very outer edge of my sorrow, and the tears
are falling like leaves at my feet in my garden chair. *(Weeps)*
O fates, O friendly providence - won't you change your tune?

*(The Brothers Twain suddenly land at her feet like a bomb.
They are special delivery and still reeking from the rat-
infested straw)*

GEORGE.   Mother!

BRUCE.   Mother!

QUEEN.   It is my sons! *(Embraces are in order)*
My goodness, aren't you smelly?

GEORGE.   So would you be, Mother, if you'd wintered in our
quarters!

BRUCE.   Oh it was nae bad.   A bit more of a vassal existence.
I think it did us good, Mother.   It was a fine experience.

GEORGE.   If it was so fine, why did you gnaw your chains?
Bruce used to gnaw his chains, Mother.

BRUCE.   Ach - they were muckle black shame tae a prince!

(QUEEN kisses him again for that)

QUEEN. Oh, I'm so happy. Now you had better go and have lovely hot baths. Oh, there are maidens from Cathay and Greenland - did you know? What joy to see my sons again - I'll have the details later. I am afraid to ask you what has happened to Roland and his Burd Ellen.

GEORGE. HIS? *(Magnanimously)* Well - he got us out of a tight spot - I will say that. I suppose I shall have to back down there.

BRUCE. They're on their way, Mother. They're coming by road, though. Mother, it's a bra' thing to fly through the air - ye canna imagine the feeling. -

QUEEN. Such joy! But do get bathed, darlings!

(Hustles them off)

Scene Five - The Throne Room of Grampia.

(Two thrones - one is covered with a dust sheet, cobwebs etc., for the King has been away for twenty years, as you know.
The QUEEN crosses to sit in the other and we cross a week or so in time.)

QUEEN. We cross a week or so in time. For time HAS meaning here.

(Her Court assembles. To start with it is visitors.
Trumpets and tuckets - enter the PRINCESS OF CATHAY. She is very nice. She has a touch of the well-known Turkish Delight advertisement about her. Frankie Howerd would have used her after his fashion. She is, in short, a dish . . . .
Enter, the other way, the ICE MAIDEN. She is very nice too. She is very furry, just the thing to warm your toes against in an igloo.)

Now all have returned from wanderings save one. And I don't mind telling you, dear Ice Princess and dear Princess of Cathay, that the continued absence of my First Counsellor hasn't helped

me to get things properly sorted out according to protocol. I
hope you haven't been put to any embarrassment. My boys are
awkward at times. They're very anxious to marry you, that
goes without saying. Mingled springs of royal blood will spout.
Oh dear, I wish I knew how to say these things! I usually just
smile, and leave the announcements to Merlin.

*(ROLAND and ELLEN have come in D/S. They are having an
interesting conversation which they continue slightly longer
than is polite on this sort of occasion. The QUEEN gives
them a look.)*

ROLAND. We think we know how to get him back, Mother!
Ellen and I have just been discussing the very problem you
mention.

QUEEN. One moment, dear - I think the boys are very anxious -
(Looks around) George! Bruce! They might have made the
effort to be on time -

*(The Court makes way. Court Servants - among whom we
discern COWIE and ISLA - fall back for the High Prince and the
Prince Preparent, who sweep in superbly. The visiting girls
look quite interested.)*

PRINCESS OF CATHAY. His eyes glisten - how proud is the
cage of his throat! His arms are liquid and his hands are foam!

QUEEN. Which one do you mean, dear?

GEORGE. Well, with the best will in the world, Mother, I should
hardly have thought that was a description of our Bruce.
(Laughs merrily)

BRUCE. Get awa'! I'm no as grabbie as some.

GEORGE. Come, come! You mustn't stare so silly.

BRUCE. She's paralysed your eyelids, that one! I like the
furry one.

QUEEN. Speak like Princes, please! Forgive them, my dears.
Courtly tones will tell - they've been away with the elves, you
know. But Roland, the youngest and dearest of all my children,
brought them back. The Princess Ellen was carried away.
It has been such a fright for my loyal people!

PEOPLE. Aye - we're right glad to see ye again, Princes a'!

QUEEN. And now let Child Roland speak! The Court is listening, dear. *(To Princesses)* He is the one that's really worth listening to - my serious, gentle, modest son - let him speak now.

ROLAND. My Royal Mother - I'm not so keen to tell my tale. It is excessively long and wearisome - as was Wrang-Gaites Way itself.

ELLEN. Only the thought of me kept him going - you see.

ROLAND. But I'll tell you about the journey back!

ELLEN. It was great, really!

ROLAND. Ellen and I sped on ahead - oh we were too fast for any of the wicked imps, who would still have liked to pinch us a bit, if they could only have got hold of us! Up burn and down currie we went. By evening we were tiring a trifle, so we found a cart, and in it we placed a frolicing brown pony that ran up, chased by brownies, and the shafts were lifted by invisible hands, and the cart ran down and up and down, to the brink of a steep brae, down which it was hurled. But we were saved from mischief and ran on, holding hands, until we came to Craig Castle all dim and dark against the midnight sky. And then we knew we were not far from home. Then we passed the Manse of Birnie, where the minister and his wife and bairns were all safely bedded, and the dog barked to tell us, and the kirkyard looked eerie and dark but on we flew. And the sweat broke out on my face and I felt giddy and weak and my knee joints made me tumble, but Ellen bore me up until we reached the Muckle Downie and the narrow passage was before me, where Ellen tripped and fell so thereafter I carried her. And so came home between the devil and the deep sea, and the greencoated imps laughed and thronged round us even to the last. And that is my true story.

BRUCE. Hoo hoo! A modest tale, says a'! Goup-a-liftie! Ye came hame by the back o' beyont, then?

ELLEN. And we climbed into the clouds, and ran through

abandoned palaces and heard the cockle's call and danced with the dawn ghosts, - so there!

ROLAND. It was great!

QUEEN. And we learn, little Princesses, of other marvels, the rescue of thralled souls. Are they not present? Let them make themselves known to us!

(ISLA and COWIE step forward)

My old domestics - welcome back to Grampia!

Have you been here long?

ISLA. We came as brisk as we could, but it was a plodding long way, Mother Majesty.

COWIE. Happy to serve our mistress royal once more, your mothership!

QUEEN. How nice. You were a great help to Child Roland, I know. But was there not a third?

ROLAND. Yes - there was a third. An honourable, noble knight, that companionship gave in the way to the Dark Tower.

COWIE. As to him we couldn't rightly say.

ISLA. It's a bit of a mystery, Madam Majesty. He seemed to slip off. Time we'd dived into the Royal Kitchens, he'd drifted away.

(Trumpets, sennets and silver trills echo throughout the Palace of Grampia. All look terrifically expectant. You don't get trumpets, sennets and trills for just anyone. Even the QUEEN sits forward and holds her breath. Centre Stage Up Stage curtains or double doors are thrown wide and there before us stands GILES SCANDANNA, the King of Grampia.)

COWIE and ISLA *(Together)* Sir Tarnash!

ROLAND. Can it be - my father?

GEORGE and BRUCE. Can it be our father?

QUEEN. My King! My husband Giles Scandanna, restored at last!

(KING is hugely embraced all round with frantic trilling and trumpeting. The dust sheet is whipped away, he ascends his throne. He probably stands on his throne in his excess of joy)

KING. And never will I go again chasing palace visitors
wrang-gaites round the Scanda Stone!

(The Princesses of Greenland and Cathay and Avalon and the
three Brothers and the King and Queen and all the people dance
Strathspeys all over the stage.

But what of MERLIN?

The Dancers subside)

Now there is one thing left to do. You must all go to sleep
immediately - and you must dream like anything. Merlin got
into the Dark Tower of the King of Elfland through my son
Roland's dream, when we were in the Petrified Forest. He will
return through yours. Dream! DREAM!

(They all compose themselves for sleep except BURD ELLEN)

Conduct this yawning orchestra, dream-burd Ellen!

ELLEN. We women will sing and you will dream! *(To ROLAND)*
That's all you're good for!

(So manly heads are laid on appropriate laps for the lullaby q.v.
It works!

MERLIN runs as fast as a nine hundred year old warlock may
down through the theatre and gets onto the stage somehow and
gets his breath back after the last lull of the by of the three
princesses and the QUEEN and the Women of Grampia.

MERLIN kneels. He kisses the KING's hand and the QUEEN's
hand)

KING. Rise, Merlin!

MERLIN. Thank you, thank you. *(Rises)* Wake up, everybody,
wake up! It was a most comfortable trip. And I've got some
really good First Counsellor work ahead now, I can just see!
The years have fallen from me! I, Merlin Caledonius, will
attend to the business of the hour.   And every hour to come!
What with one thing and another, I'm going to be busy! I'll
soon set about those scallawags and Dundees, your Majesty!
I'll soon arrange the most model marriages for Princes and
Princesses! You needn't worry about anything!   Your
Majesties, you needn't . . . . . needn't . . . .

(His voice trails off. He has forgotten it all again)
PEOPLE. But you've forgotten everything!
(MERLIN puts his head in his hands.
ELLEN comforts him as the curtain falls.)

END OF PLAY

Slimline Version for Company of Six

CHIEF ROLES :
  GEORGE, BRUCE, ROLAND, ELLEN, QUEEN, MERLIN

SUBSIDIARY ROLES :
  GEORGE also plays HORSEHERD (SIR TARNASH), ELF KING
                      (EEK), and KING OF GRAMPIA.
  BRUCE also plays COWHERD (COWIE) and PORTER OF THE
                      DARK TOWER.
  ROLAND doesn't play anything else.
  ELLEN plays OLD WOMAN
  QUEEN plays HENWIFE (ISLA)
  MERLIN plays CRIPPLE

PAGE NOTES :

18   THE PEOPLE are *made of cardboard* and have been
      standing D.R. since curtain rise.   The stage manager has
      devised a way of making their eyes roll.   They can also wave
      flags with a little help.   Cheering crowds are O/S

19·   THE SERVANTS/PALACE GUARD are *made of card-*
      board.   They have been standing D.L. since curtain rise.
      They are pulled on.

20   THE **DRUMMER** is *made of cardboard* and is pulled on.
      The servant's voice during the arming of GEORGE is done by
      ROLAND in a funny voice.

35   We boldly CUT the FOREST SCENE, substituting for
      it a MIME of the Companions lost in the Petrified Forest.   The
      DREAM goes as well, and this is a more serious loss, but not
      a fatal one.

54   EEK is played by actor playing GEORGE - in a horrible
      mask.   As in the end he becomes the King of Grampia it is
      quite in keeping that he should do the Elf King (EEK) as well.
      (The High Prince could become noble or nasty upon his access-
      ion - moral spin-off here).

55   BRUCE's further transformation (from CowHerd COWIE to PORTER of Dark Gate) is substantiated, and in keeping with his brawny soul. As the actors are engaged otherwise, and can't still be themselves, the Brothers Twain are not seen, but the dungeon bars are simulated for ELLEN to kneel by.

59   The fun here is that our brilliant actor plays both parts, jumping out of one of his skins into another in a most praise-worthy and funny way.

62   SIR TARNASH chases a MONSTER O/S early on, so he can come back in his EEK mask. The MONSTERS are invisible; the battle with them is mimed.

68   The Visiting PRINCESSES are not seen. This is how it goes : The PRINCES look O/S. QUEEN says 'Well, what do you think of them?', pauses for Princesses' answer, and then says 'Which one do you mean, dear?' And the rest runs.

70   ISLA and COWIE are not visible but their voices have been recorded so we are not stymied by our smallness of cast at the last lap, and instead we have the brilliant tour de force of the actress playing QUEEN answering her own voice as ISLA and the actor playing BRUCE answering his own voice as COWIE.

70   Finally, all GEORGE needs in order to become his royal dad is the Crown - which the stage manager will have kept handy.

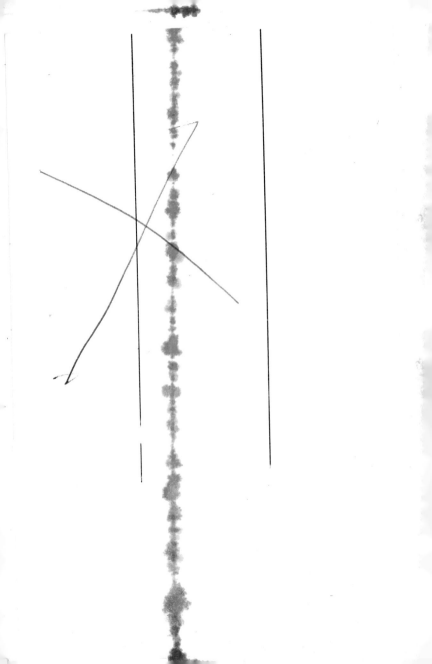